The Things I Wish She Said

A Guided Journal for Mothers and Daughters to Build a Stronger Relationship

The Things I Wish She Said

Dedication

To my sons who are my constant motivators I will always speak life into you. Dia, I thank you for your continuous encouragement and support. Thank you for always supporting my dreams. To my bestie Shanell that always have my back and gives me her honest opinion. Chanel thank you for always being there when I need you.

Love,

-Michel Harris

Introduction

I created this therapeutic writing journal to be a safe place to reflect your thoughts and feelings. This journal can be used as a communication tool between moms and daughters to freely express themselves. Recording in this journal will help enhance, strengthen and rebuild healthy relationships, with your mother or daughters.
If you are new to journaling and confused about where to begin, no worries, each page includes a prompt to inspire your feelings.

How to use I Wish She Said: from a daughters perspective if you are the one journaling you would read the entire guided prompt and record your thoughts and feelings in relation to that prompt. If you are mom journaling you would read just the end prompts and begin journaling. The tear away pages are to be completed by both mom and daughter to enhance and strengthen their relationships. Complete with affirmations and self-check lists.
Example:
I Wish She Said: I will encourage you in everything that you do:

Daughter would journal about all the things she wish her mom would say to encourage her
Mom would journal about all the ways she could encourage her daughter.

I hope this journal will be a help tool in your familial relationships. There are times when it is hard to listen to another person's point of view, but when that message is written and we can see that person's intentions without feeling judged or ridiculed that information is easier to accept and understand.

-Michel Harris

Journal Guide

Hello and welcome to the world of journaling. I hope this will be a fun and exciting experience.

Q: What is Journaling
A: A way to express your thoughts and feelings freely through writing

Q: How do I choose a topic
A: Some journals come with writing prompts, other journals just allow you to express freely. You can be as descriptive or creative as you like. Just grab a pencil or pen and write what feels good to you.

This journal comes with positive affirmations, to encourage you. You can use it to inspire your writing. This is your new bestfriend so tell a story, write about a time that made you happy or sad, a trip you want to take. Just remember to enjoy your writing experience.

Rebuild: Your relationship by Reassuring your love for one another

Build: Your relationship by Communicating Effectively

Strengthen: Your relationship by Having Meaningful Conversations

Enhance: Your relationship by Connecting with daily Hugs, Kisses, and Positive Affirmations

I Wish She Said: Can you forgive me

_____
_____
_____
_____
_____
_____
_____
_____
_____
_____
_____
_____
_____
_____
_____
_____
_____
_____
_____
_____
_____
_____
_____

I Wish She Said: I Love this about you

_____

_____

_____

_____

_____

_____

_____

_____

_____

_____

_____

_____

_____

_____

_____

_____

_____

_____

_____

_____

_____

_____

_____

_____

I Wish She Said: Use good judgement

I Wish She Said: Education is the key

_____

_____

_____

_____

_____

_____

_____

_____

_____

_____

_____

_____

_____

_____

_____

_____

_____

_____

_____

_____

_____

_____

_____

_____

I Wish She Said: How can I help you

_____
_____
_____
_____
_____
_____
_____
_____
_____
_____
_____
_____
_____
_____
_____
_____
_____
_____
_____
_____
_____
_____
_____

I Wish She Said: I will protect your heart

_____

_____

_____

_____

_____

_____

_____

_____

_____

_____

_____

_____

_____

_____

_____

_____

_____

_____

_____

_____

_____

_____

_____

Create a safe
place where your
thoughts and
feelings can
equally be heard
without judgement.

I Wish She Said: I will treat you the way you deserve to be treated

_____

_____

_____

_____

_____

_____

_____

_____

_____

_____

_____

_____

_____

_____

_____

_____

_____

_____

_____

_____

_____

_____

I Wish She Said: Trust your instincts. I trust you

I Wish She Said: Do not make the same mistakes I made

Having Open and Honest
Communication is the Key to every
Healthy Relationship. Ask yourselves:
Where Should We Start?

I Wish She Said: I will help you understand the things you don't

I Wish She Said: Respect yourself and others

_____
_____
_____
_____
_____
_____
_____
_____
_____
_____
_____
_____
_____
_____
_____
_____
_____
_____
_____
_____
_____
_____
_____

I Wish She Said: I will always be here for you

Daughters are reflections of their mothers. Make it A good one!

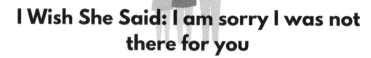

I Wish She Said: I am sorry I was not there for you

_____
_____
_____
_____
_____
_____
_____
_____
_____
_____
_____
_____
_____
_____
_____
_____
_____
_____
_____
_____
_____
_____
_____
_____

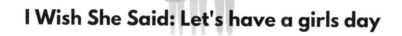

I Wish She Said: Let's have a girls day

I Wish She Said: You can do anything you put your mind too

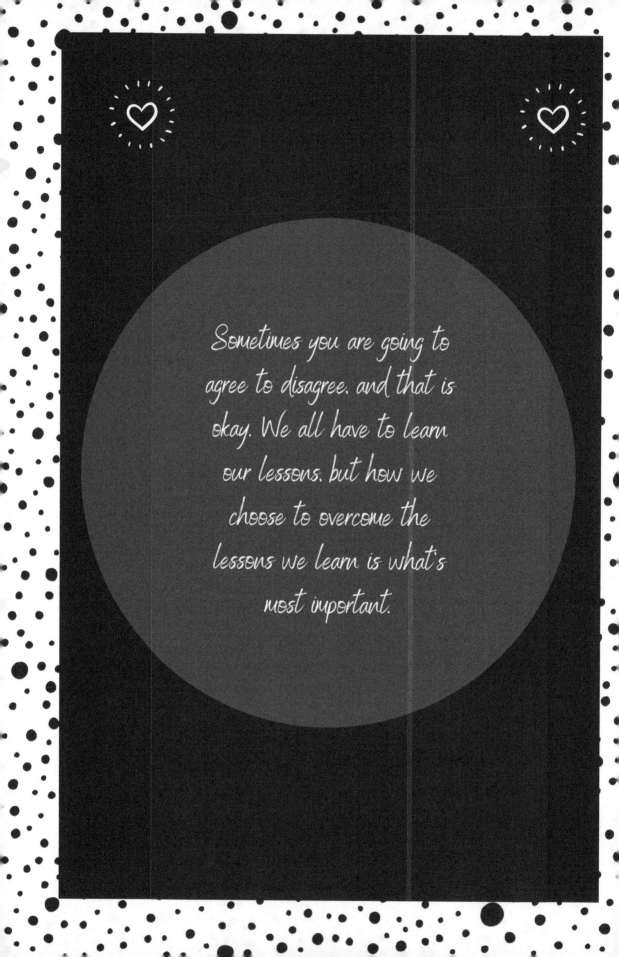

Sometimes you are going to agree to disagree, and that is okay. We all have to learn our lessons, but how we choose to overcome the lessons we learn is what's most important.

I Wish She Said: I will protect you

_____
_____
_____
_____
_____
_____
_____
_____
_____
_____
_____
_____
_____
_____
_____
_____
_____
_____
_____
_____
_____
_____

I Wish She Said: I will never put drinking or drugs before you

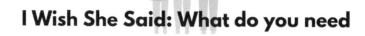

I Wish She Said: What do you need

_____
_____
_____
_____
_____
_____
_____
_____
_____
_____
_____
_____
_____
_____
_____
_____
_____
_____
_____
_____
_____
_____
_____
_____

I Wish She Said: You can always count on me

I Wish She Said: Trust yourself

_____
_____
_____
_____
_____
_____
_____
_____
_____
_____
_____
_____
_____
_____
_____
_____
_____
_____
_____
_____
_____

I Wish She Said: Be kind to others

_____

_____

_____

_____

_____

_____

_____

_____

_____

_____

_____

_____

_____

_____

_____

_____

_____

_____

_____

_____

_____

_____

_____

_____

_____

Help her
understand your
point of view.
Your perspective
may be valid!

I Wish She Said: Choose a career you will love, not for the money

_____

_____

_____

_____

_____

_____

_____

_____

_____

_____

_____

_____

_____

_____

_____

_____

_____

_____

_____

_____

_____

_____

_____

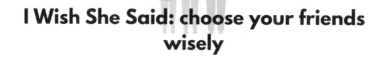

I Wish She Said: choose your friends wisely

_____

_____

_____

_____

_____

_____

_____

_____

_____

_____

_____

_____

_____

_____

_____

_____

_____

_____

_____

_____

_____

_____

I Wish She Said: Build a healthy spiritual relationship

_____
_____
_____
_____
_____
_____
_____
_____
_____
_____
_____
_____
_____
_____
_____
_____
_____
_____
_____
_____
_____
_____

I Wish She Said: Make good choices with your finances

_____

_____

_____

_____

_____

_____

_____

_____

_____

_____

_____

_____

_____

_____

_____

_____

_____

_____

_____

_____

_____

_____

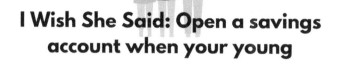

I Wish She Said: Open a savings account when your young

I Wish She Said: Love yourself first before anyone else

_____

_____

_____

_____

_____

_____

_____

_____

_____

_____

_____

_____

_____

_____

_____

_____

_____

_____

_____

_____

_____

_____

_____

CONFLICTS WILL HAPPEN

It is our instinct to protect ourselves when we feel attacked or threatened. When a loved one says something we don't like, or we feel is valid, we as humans tend to shut down and stop listening. Oftentimes, we miss the point of the message being communicated. "It is not always what you say, but how you say it." A written message allows both sides to get their points across without being interrupted and decrease the chance of either person being offended. Practicing humility and understanding can go along way when you take you out of the situation. Look at what is being communicated and turn that situation into a positive reinforcement to mature and grow.

I Wish She Said: Accept who you are, because I accept you first

_____

_____

_____

_____

_____

_____

_____

_____

_____

_____

_____

_____

_____

_____

_____

_____

_____

_____

_____

_____

_____

_____

_____

I Wish She Said: Be trustworthy and I will be a person you can trust

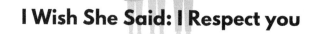

I Wish She Said: I Respect you

_____
_____
_____
_____
_____
_____
_____
_____
_____
_____
_____
_____
_____
_____
_____
_____
_____
_____
_____
_____
_____
_____
_____
_____
_____

There is no love like
A mother and child

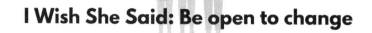

I Wish She Said: Be open to change

_____

_____

_____

_____

_____

_____

_____

_____

_____

_____

_____

_____

_____

_____

_____

_____

_____

_____

_____

_____

_____

_____

_____

_____

_____

I Wish She Said: You are enough, your truly amazing

I Wish She Said: Never settle for anything

_____
_____
_____
_____
_____
_____
_____
_____
_____
_____
_____
_____
_____
_____
_____
_____
_____
_____
_____
_____
_____
_____
_____
_____

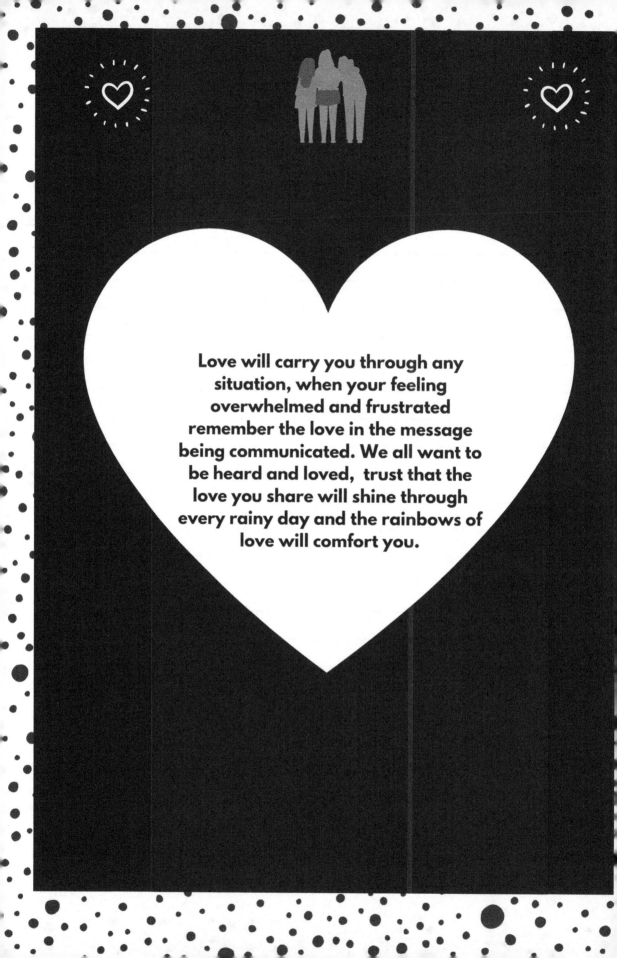

Love will carry you through any situation, when your feeling overwhelmed and frustrated remember the love in the message being communicated. We all want to be heard and loved, trust that the love you share will shine through every rainy day and the rainbows of love will comfort you.

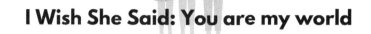

I Wish She Said: You are my world

_____
_____
_____
_____
_____
_____
_____
_____
_____
_____
_____
_____
_____
_____
_____
_____
_____
_____
_____
_____
_____
_____
_____
_____
_____
_____

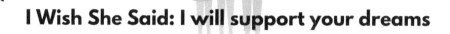

I Wish She Said: I will support your dreams

_____

_____

_____

_____

_____

_____

_____

_____

_____

_____

_____

_____

_____

_____

_____

_____

_____

_____

_____

_____

I Wish She Said: I will teach you to be the woman you were destined to be

_____
_____
_____
_____
_____
_____
_____
_____
_____
_____
_____
_____
_____
_____
_____
_____
_____
_____
_____
_____
_____
_____
_____
_____
_____

Commit to spending 20 minutes a day together, talking and listening to each other. Block out distractions, television, telephones, and social media.

Have hard conversations, but end it in a positive way.

Reassure your love for one another

I Wish She Said: I will think before I speak

I Wish She Said: Keep calm, don't over-react

_____

_____

_____

_____

_____

_____

_____

_____

_____

_____

_____

_____

_____

_____

_____

_____

_____

_____

_____

_____

_____

_____

_____

I Wish She Said: I will encourage you in everything that you do

_____

_____

_____

_____

_____

_____

_____

_____

_____

_____

_____

_____

_____

_____

_____

_____

_____

_____

_____

_____

_____

_____

I Wish She Said: Write your short and long term goals and let's face them together

_____
_____
_____
_____
_____
_____
_____
_____
_____
_____
_____
_____
_____
_____
_____
_____
_____
_____
_____
_____
_____
_____
_____

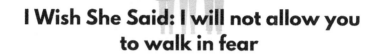

I Wish She Said: I will not allow you to walk in fear

_____

_____

_____

_____

_____

_____

_____

_____

_____

_____

_____

_____

_____

_____

_____

_____

_____

_____

_____

_____

_____

_____

_____

_____

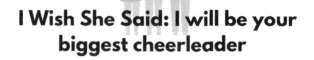

I Wish She Said: I will be your biggest cheerleader

Love is Pure and
Cleanses the Soul.
Forgive and Move On

I Wish She Said: I didn't mean to hurt you

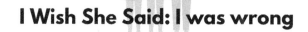

I Wish She Said: I was wrong

_____

_____

_____

_____

_____

_____

_____

_____

_____

_____

_____

_____

_____

_____

_____

_____

_____

_____

_____

_____

_____

_____

_____

_____

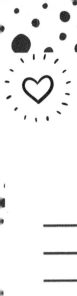

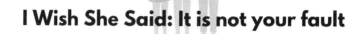

I Wish She Said: It is not your fault

_____

_____

_____

_____

_____

_____

_____

_____

_____

_____

_____

_____

_____

_____

_____

_____

_____

_____

_____

_____

_____

_____

_____

I Wish She Said: I understand how you feel

I hope you will find the following exercises helpful. They are to be completed by mom and daughter. Just cut them out and be transparent with each other and you will be surprised how helpful these exercises will be.

Feelings I would like us to explore or understand:

_____

_____

_____

_____

_____

_____

_____

_____

_____

_____

_____

_____

_____

_____

_____

_____

_____

_____

_____

_____

_____

I felt criticized when you:

_____

_____

_____

_____

_____

_____

_____

_____

_____

_____

I really don't like when you said:

_____

_____

_____

_____

_____

_____

_____

_____

_____

_____

How do it make you feel when I:

_____
_____
_____
_____
_____
_____
_____
_____
_____
_____

What can we do to improve:

_____
_____
_____
_____
_____
_____
_____
_____
_____
_____

I really don't like when you:

_____
_____
_____
_____
_____
_____
_____
_____
_____
_____
_____

This made me feel:

_____
_____
_____
_____
_____
_____
_____
_____
_____
_____
_____

I Believe in you:

_____
_____
_____
_____
_____
_____
_____
_____
_____
_____
_____
_____
_____

You love when I:

_____
_____
_____
_____
_____
_____
_____
_____
_____
_____
_____
_____

MOM & DAUGHTER EXERCISE----------CUT HERE

You are so good at:

_____
_____
_____
_____
_____
_____
_____
_____
_____
_____

I really admire you:

_____
_____
_____
_____
_____
_____
_____
_____
_____
_____

Fill in a thought _____

_____
_____
_____
_____
_____
_____
_____
_____
_____
_____

Fill in a thought _____

_____
_____
_____
_____
_____
_____
_____
_____
_____
_____
_____

Mom's Checklist

☐ **I show my daughter unconditional love:**

☐ **I do not force my thoughts and views on her:**

☐ **I encourage her to be amazing:**

☐ **I support her goals and dreams:**

Things I can work on to enhance our relationship:

_____

_____

_____

_____

_____

_____

_____

_____

_____

Fill in a thought _____

_____
_____
_____
_____
_____
_____
_____
_____
_____
_____
_____

Fill in a thought _____

_____
_____
_____
_____
_____
_____
_____
_____
_____
_____
_____
_____
_____

Mom's Checklist

☐ **I make my daughter a priority:**

☐ **I help her figure out tough situations:**

☐ **I don't criticize or belittle her:**

☐ **I listen without judgement:**

Things I can work on to enhance our relationship:

_____

_____

_____

_____

_____

_____

_____

_____

_____

Fill in a thought _____

_____
_____
_____
_____
_____
_____
_____
_____
_____
_____
_____

Fill in a thought _____

_____
_____
_____
_____
_____
_____
_____
_____
_____
_____
_____
_____

Daughter's Checklist

☐ **I show my mother unconditional love:**

☐ **I spend quality time with her:**

☐ **I tell her how I am feeling:**

☐ **I respect her point of view even if I
don't agree with her:**

Things I can work on to enhance our relationship:

_____
_____
_____
_____
_____
_____
_____
_____
_____
_____
_____

Fill in a thought _____

_____
_____
_____
_____
_____
_____
_____
_____
_____
_____
_____
_____

Fill in a thought _____

_____
_____
_____
_____
_____
_____
_____
_____
_____
_____
_____
_____
_____

CUT HERE.....MOM & DAUGHTER EXERCISE----------CUT HERE

Daughter's Checklist

☐ **I listen to how she is feeling:**

☐ **I offer to help her when I can:**

☐ **I don't have unrealistic expectations**

☐ **I respect her:**

Things I can work on to enhance our relationship:

_____

_____

_____

_____

_____

_____

_____

_____

_____

_____

Fill in a thought _____

_____
_____
_____
_____
_____
_____
_____
_____
_____
_____
_____
_____

Fill in a thought _____

_____
_____
_____
_____
_____
_____
_____
_____
_____
_____
_____

CUT HERE......MOM & DAUGHTER EXERCISE------------CUT HERE

Fill in a thought _____

_____
_____
_____
_____
_____
_____
_____
_____
_____
_____
_____
_____

Fill in a thought _____

_____
_____
_____
_____
_____
_____
_____
_____
_____
_____
_____
_____

Made in the USA
Monee, IL
27 January 2022

89967823R00083